CAMPFIRE SONGS 2

COMPILED BY PAUL TAYLOR

COVER DESIGN AND ILLUSTRATION BY

RON BRANAGAN

© Printforce Limited

British Library Cataloguing in Publication Data
Taylor, Paul
     Campfire songs two.
     1.   Children's songs in English
     I.   Title
     782.42

     ISBN 0-948834-46-3

CONTENTS

INTRODUCTION

Campfire resource books are among the most popular Printforce publications, and we hope that readers will find this second volume of Campfire Songs as useful as the other books mentioned below.

We have tried to avoid infringing copyright, but should any mistake have been made, we apologise and will be pleased to make any necessary amendment in future editions.

The other Printforce Campfire books listed below, together with this book, form a unique resource for planning a Campfire or other occasion when entertainment is required.

We wish you successful singing!

Paul Taylor

Campfire Songs 1
Campfire Stunts 1
Campfire Stunts 2
Campfire Fun
The Campfire Companion

OPENING AND CLOSING SONGS

COME ON AND SING WITH ME

1.   Come on and sing with me, hey dee roon oh
     Come on and sing with me, hey dee roon oh
     Come on and sing with me, hey dee roon oh
     Come on and sing with me, hey dee roon oh

Chorus (to the same tune as the verse)

     Sing everybody sing, hey dee roon oh......

2.   Come and and clap with me......

3.   Come on and click with me......

4.   Come and and stamp with me......

5.   Come on and stretch with me......

(Add actions in the verses to suit the words, and just sing in the choruses. Add other verses if you wish).

I'M SO GLAD

1. I'm so glad we're meeting here tonight
   I'm so glad we're meeting here tonight
   I'm so glad we're meeting here tonight
   Sing glory hallelujah, I'm so glad.

2. I'm so glad we're singing round the fire......

3. I'm so glad we're brothers everyone......

4. I'm so glad we're travelling life's road......

5. I'm so glad we're happy to be here......

(You may be able to make up suitable verses for your own group or occasion).

GOODNIGHT CAMPERS

Goodnight campers, goodnight campers,
Goodnight campers, it's time to say goodnight.
Sadly it is time to part, time to part, time to part.
Sadly it is time to part, and to say goodnight.

(To create extra verses, other words can be substituted for
campers, e.g. Cub Scouts, Guides, Leaders, or whatever suits
your own group of singers).

ALL NIGHT, ALL DAY

1.   All night, all day
Angels watching over me, my Lord
All night, all day
Angels watching over me.

2.   Now I lay me down to sleep
Angels watching over me, my Lord
Pray the Lord my soul to keep
Angels watching over me.

3.   If I die before I wake
Angels watching over me, my Lord
Pray the Lord my soul to take
Angels watching over me.

4.   If I live forever and a day
Angels watching over me, my Lord
Pray the Lord guard me all the way
Angels watching over me.

KUM BA YAH

This sung prayer is often used at the end of a camp fire. The suggested verses can be altered to suit the occasion. The harmony part given is not difficult to sing, and is effective. The last verses draw the camp fire to a quiet and reverent close.

1.   Kum ba yah, my Lord, kum ba yah
   Kum ba yah, my Lord, kum ba yah
   Kum ba yah, my Lord, kum ba yah
   O Lord, kum ba yah.

2.   Someone's singing, Lord....

3.   Someone's laughing, Lord....

4.   Someone's crying, Lord....

5.   Come by here, my Lord....

WHAT A GRAND AND GLORIOUS FEELING

The theme of this short song is friendship and peace, which suits the end of a camp fire. It can be sung as a three part round, with the sound of the bells fading away gently at the end.

What a grand and glorious feeling, glorious feeling
When the bells of peace are ringing, peace are ringing
Peace on earth, peace on earth, peace on earth.

ACTION SONGS

IF YOU'RE HAPPY AND YOU KNOW IT

1. If you're happy and you know it, clap your hands (G) (D7)
(CLAP, CLAP)

   If you're happy and you know it, clap your hands (G)
(CLAP, CLAP)

   If you're happy and you know it, and you really want to show it, (C) (G)

   If you're happy and you know it, clap your hands (D7) (G)
(CLAP, CLAP)

2. If you're happy and you know it, stamp your feet....

3. If you're happy and you know it, click your fingers....

4. If you're happy and you know it, nod your head....

5. If you're happy and you know it, say "We are!"....

6. If you're happy and you know it, do all five (CLAP CLAP, STAMP STAMP, CLICK CLICK, NOD NOD, "WE ARE!")...

(Adjust the number of verses and the type of action to suit your own group).

OLD MACDONALD

This version of a well-known song comes with actions!

1. Old Macdonald had a farm, ee-i, ee-i, oh
    And on that farm he had a cow, ee-i, ee-i, oh.

    Big cow, little cow, little cow, big cow,
    Fat cow, thin cow, thin cow, fat cow.
    Old Macdonald had a farm, ee-i, ee-i, oh.

2. And on that farm he had a pig, ee-i, ee-i, oh.

    Big pig, little pig, little pig, big pig,
    Fat pig, thin pig, thin pig, fat pig.
    Big cow, little cow, little cow, big cow,
    Fat cow, thin cow, thin cow, fat cow.
    Old Macdonald had a farm, ee-i, ee-i, oh.

3. And on that farm he had....(ask the group for the next animal).

Actions

Everyone uses their hands to show the size of the animals.

On each word "big" do this:

On each word "little" do this:

On each word "fat" do this:

On each word "thin" do this:

Five successive animals are usually enough for the leader to show off his or her skill with the actions (practise first!), and for the rest of the singers to give up in confusion. If your group has done it all before, catch them out by reversing the actions (little = big, etc!).

OKKI TOKKI OOMPAH

This is supposedly an Eskimo song about hunting seals. The leader tells the story of the seal hunt as the song proceeds.

"One day a party of Eskimos set off in their kayaks to catch seals. As they paddled, they sang:"

Chorus   Okki tokki oompah, okki tokki oompah
Hey diddle, hi diddle, ho diddle, hey.

(Everyone paddles as they sing the chorus - fold arms and lower elbows alternately to left and right)

1.   "They looked hard for seals, to the east and to the west, and as they looked they sang:"

Hey tokala mushuaki   (With hand over eyes, look
Hey tokala mushuaki   from side to side)
Hey tokala mushuaki

"At last they spotted some, and paddled towards them." (Chorus)

2.   "When they got near, they threw their heavy harpoons, singing:"

Hey tokala mushuaki. Uhh!   (Mime the throws, to
Hey tokala mushuaki. Uhh!   one side and the
Hey tokala mushuaki. Uhh!   other)

"Then they loaded their catch, and paddled for home." (Chorus)

3.   "As they got near, they waved to their friends on shore, singing:"

Hey tokala mushuaki. (Wave - one hand)
Hey tokala mushuaki. (Wave - the other hand)

Hey tokala mushuaki. (Wave - the first hand again)

"Then they paddled to the shore at top speed." (Chorus - fast!)

MY BONNIE LIES OVER THE OCEAN

My b^Gonnie lies ^Cover the o^Gcean

My bonnie lies ^{A7}over the ^{D7}sea

My b^Gonnie lies ^Cover the o^Gcean

Oh b^{Am}ring back my bonnie ^{D7}to ^Gme.

Bri^Gng back, bri^{Am}ng back,

Oh b^Dring back my bonnie to ^Gme, ^Dto ^Gme.

Bri^Gng back, bri^{Am}ng back,

Oh b^Dring back my bon^{D7}nie to ^Gme.

Each main word in the song has an action, listed below. The challenge is simply to match the actions to the words all the way through. As you get better, you try it faster!

Actions

my	-	touch your own chest
bonnie	-	fold arms (a reminder of an embrace)
lies	-	make a pillow with both hands
over	-	draw a bridge in the air
ocean	-	draw waves in the air
sea	-	draw waves in the air
bring back	-	extend both arms on 'bring'; on 'back' draw them towards you in a beckoning gesture

Optional extras:

oh	-	make an O shape with thumbs and index fingers
to	-	show two fingers

SHE'LL BE COMING ROUND THE MOUNTAIN

In this action version, add spoken words and matching actions at the end of lines as indicated. As each new action is added, repeat the previous actions as well.

1.   Action - pull down handle to make train whistle

She'll be $\overset{G}{\text{coming}}$ round the mountain when she comes
Whoo whoo!

She'll be coming round the mountain when she $\overset{D7}{\text{comes}}$
Whoo whoo!

She'll be $\overset{G}{\text{coming}}$ round the mountain, $\overset{C}{\text{coming}}$ round the mountain,

$\overset{G}{\text{Coming}}$ round the $\overset{D7}{\text{mountain}}$ when she $\overset{G}{\text{comes}}$.
Whoo whoo!

2.   Action - pull back on horses' reins

She'll be driving six white horses when she comes.
Whoa back!
Whoo whoo!

3.   Action - draw circle in front of face, palm outwards

And we'll all go out to meet her when she comes.
Hi babe!
Whoa back!
Whoo whoo!

4.   Action - rub tummy

And we'll all have stew and dumplings when she comes.
Yum yum!
Hi babe!
Whoa back!
Whoo whoo!

There is also an optional chorus between verses:

Singing aye-aye-yippy-yippy-aye
Singing aye-aye-yippy-yippy-aye
Singing aye-aye-yippy, aye-aye-yippy,
Aye-aye-yippy-yippy-aye.

ONE FINGER, ONE THUMB

In this song, each time a part of the body is mentioned, every-one moves that part.

1. One finger, one thumb, keep moving
   One finger, one thumb, keep moving
   One finger, one thumb, keep moving
   We'll all be merry and bright.

2. One finger, one thumb, one arm, one leg, keep moving...

3. One finger, one thumb, one arm, one leg, one nod of the head, keep moving...

4. One finger, one thumb, one arm, one leg, one nod of the head, stand up, sit down, keep moving...

If the singers are still with you, challenge them with verse 5, slowly at first, but getting faster:

5. Two fingers, two thumbs, two arms, two legs, two nods of the head, stand up, sit down, stand up, sit down, keep moving...

ALOUETTE

To lead this song, it helps to know some parts of the body in French!

Chorus   Alouette, gentille Alouette,
                Alouette, je te plumerai.

1.   **Leader**   Je te plumerai la tete
     Singers   Je te plumerai la tete
     Leader   Et la tete
     Singers   Et la tete
     Leader   Alouette
     Singers   Alouette. Ohhhhhh... (Chorus)

2.   **Leader**   Je te plumerai le nez

3.   **Etc.**

Each time the leader mentions a part of the body, he points to it. When the singers mention it, they point. As the song builds up, it becomes a game of memory and of agility!

French translation

la tete	=	head	la main	=	hand
le nez	=	nose	la jambe	=	leg
la bouche	=	mouth	le pied	=	foot
le bras	=	arm			

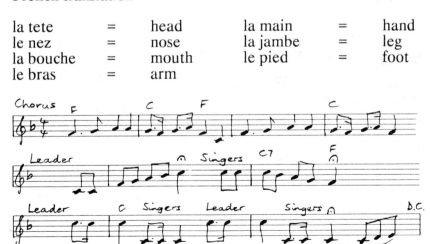

21

ONI WONI WONI WAH WAH

Oni-woni-woni wah-wah
Oni-woni-woni wah-wah
Aye-aye-aye-yippy aye-aye-yarky
aye-aye-aye-yippy aye-aye
Aye-aye

To teach this nonsense song, begin with the first set of actions, which start with arms folded in front of you as shown on the next page.

Then try the second set of actions, which uses only two index fingers as shown.

Next learn the tune and the words, and practise them a few times. Then try singing it with the actions learnt so far.

There are two other sets of actions. To start set 3, hold your left ear with your right hand, and put your left hand on your nose! Then move left hand to right ear, and right hand to nose. That's all there is to it! Just repeat throughout the verse.

Set 4 is for singers sitting in a circle or a row. Start with both hands on your own knees. In rhythm, move both hands one knee to your left (so your left hand taps your neighbour's knee), then back to your own, then to the right, then repeat. For even more hilarity, go two knees to the left, and then to the right!

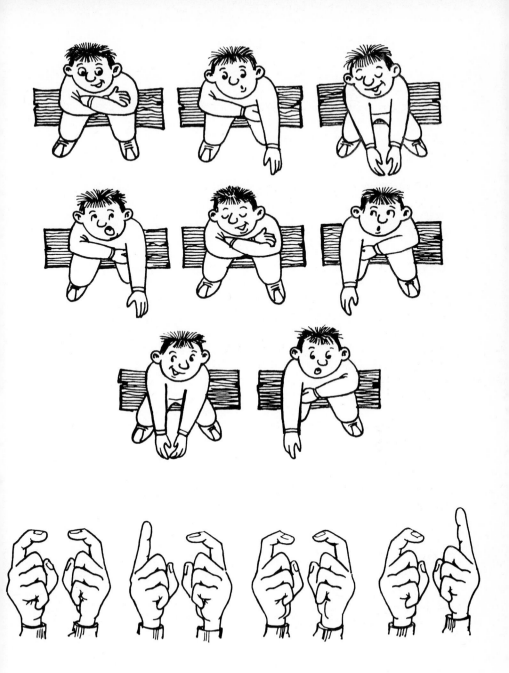

DO YOUR EARS HANG LOW?

Do your ears hang low?
Do they wobble to and fro?
Can you tie them in a knot?
Can you tie them in a bow?
Can you toss them over your shoulder
Like a regimental soldier?
Do your ears hang low?

Actions

Line 1	Put fingers on ears and mime them curling downwards
Line 2	Wobble hands to and fro in front of you
Line 3	Mime tying a knot and pulling it tight
Line 4	Mime tying a large bow
Lines 5-6	Toss both hands over one shoulder
Line 7	As line 1

REPETITIVE SONGS

ONE MAN WENT TO MOW

1.   One man went to mow
        (D)

    Went to mow a meadow.
             (A7)

    One man and his dog Spot

    Went to mow a meadow.
             (D)

2.   Two men went to mow
    Went to mow a meadow.
    Two men, one man and their dogs Spot and Patch
    Went to mow a meadow.

Continue adding men and dogs, using names such as Fred, Fido, Rover, etc.

A variation for young campers such as Cub Scouts is:

One Cub went to camp,
Went to camp at .... (Insert name of camp site)
One Cub and his Pack,.............(Insert name of Pack)
Went to camp at...........

Two Cubs went to camp....

And so on.

THERE'S A HOLE IN MY BUCKET

To sing this song, split the group in two, to play Liza and Henry. Let Liza's sarcastic impatience increase gradually, and let Henry enjoy his final victory!

1.   There's a hole in my bucket, dear Liza, dear Liza
             G   C   G   C   G   C

There's a a hole in my bucket, dear Liza, a hole!
      G   C   G   C   D7 G

2.   Then mend it, dear Henry, dear Henry, dear Henry

       Then mend it, dear Henry, dear Henry, mend it!

3.   With what shall I mend it?
4.   With a straw.
5.   But the straw is too long.
6.   Then cut it.
7.   With what shall I cut it?
8.   With an axe.
9.   But the axe is too blunt.
10.   Then sharpen it.
11.   On what shall I sharpen it?
12.   On a stone.
13.   But the stone is too dry.
14.   Then wet it.
15.   With what shall I wet it?
16.   With water.
17.   In what shall I fetch it?
18.   In a bucket.
19.   As verse 1!

TEN GREEN BOTTLES

Try several variations of this song, one after another. To avoid boredom with the well-known version, start at five:

E   B7   E
Five green bottles hanging on the wall

                 B7   E
Five green bottles hanging on the wall

        A   E   F#m(A)   A
And if one green bottle should accidentally fall

        E   B7   E
There'd be four green bottles hanging on the wall.

Four green bottles.....

This variation starts at ten, but the numbers decrease in twos:

Ten fat sausages sizzling in the pan
Ten fat sausages sizzling in the pan
One went pop and another went bang!
There were eight fat sausages sizzling in the pan.

Still in the kitchen, you may want to give a lesson in hygiene:

One bluebottle sitting on the meat
One bluebottle sitting on the meat
And if that bluebottle should wipe his dirty feet
Then somebody's dinner will not be fit to eat!

Finally, the version that's over as soon as it has begun:

Ten sticks of dynamite hanging on the wall
Ten sticks of dynamite hanging on the wall
And if one stick of dynamite should accidentlly fall
There'd be no sticks of dynamite and no bloomin' wall!

THREE LITTLE ANGELS

1.   Three little angels dressed in white
    Tried to get to heaven on the top of a kite.
    The kite string broke, the angels fell
    They couldn't get to heaven so they all went to...

2.   Two little angels... (as verse 1)

3.   One little angel.... (as verse 1, but in the singular)

4.   Three little devils dressed in red
    Tried to get to heaven on the top of a bed.
    The bedpost broke, the devils fell
    They couldn't get to heaven so they all went to...

5.   Two little devils....

6.   One little devil....

7.   Angels and devils, white and red
    They couldn't get to heaven so they all went to bed!

WHEN I FIRST CAME TO THIS LAND

1.   When I first came to this land
   I was not a wealthy man
   So I got myself a shack
   And I did all I could.

2.   And I called the shack "Break my back".
   But the land was sweet and good
   And I did all I could.

2.   When I first came to this land
   I was not a wealthy man
   So I got myself a cow
   And I did all I could.

   And I called my cow "No milk now"
   And I called my shack "Break my back".
   But the land was sweet and good
   And I did all I could.

Continue the pattern with successive acquisitions:

3.   Hen - "Now and then"
4.   Donkey - "Horse gone wonky"
5.   Wife - "Run for your life"
6.   Son - "My work's done"

I AM THE MUSIC MAN

1. Leader: I am the Music Man and I come from far
                away and I can play....

    Singers: What can you play?

    Leader: I play the piano.

    All: Pia, pia, piano, piano, piano,
               pia, pia, piano, pia, piano.

During the chorus, everybody mimes playing the instrument.
Repeat the words for subsequent verses, changing the instrument, and adding to the chorus, e.g.

2. Instrument: Bass drum
    Chorus: Boom, boom, boom diddy boom, etc.
                 Pia, pia, piano, etc.

3. Instrument: Trumpet
    Chorus: Toot, toot, rooty toot, etc.
                 Boom, boom, boom diddy boom, etc.
                 Pia, pia, piano, etc.

Other verses can feature the violin, trombome, harp, triangle, bagpipes, and any other instrument you fancy. Make up the chorus to suit the instrument.

ONE LITTLE ELEPHANT

During the first verse of this song, the leader stands up and pretends to be the acrobatic elephant, using one arm to represent his trunk. At the end of the verse, he chooses someone to join him, and they both mime the balancing act, trunk to tail. At the end of each verse an extra elephant is called up.

1.   One little elephant balancing
      Step by step on a piece of string.
      He thought it was a clever stunt
      So he called up another little elephant.

2.   Two little elephants balancing
      Step by step on a piece of string.
      They thought it was a clever stunt
      So they called up another little elephant.

3.   Three little elephants...

And so on. When the leader thinks enough is enough, he can sing a final verse, for example:

      Ten little elephants balancing
      Step by step on a piece of string.
      The first little elephant turned around (the leader gives
      the line a push)
      And nine little elephants all fell down!

TOMORROW WE'LL HAVE KIPPERS FOR TEA

(OR THE PATAGONIAN SHEPHERDS' SONG)

Legend tells that Patagonian shepherds regard kippers as the greatest of delicacies. They also have a form of greeting peculiar to themselves, influenced a little by their flocks. Two shepherds stand facing each other. The first jumps in the air, bending his legs at the knees and simultaneously raising both hands to the position of horns, while shouting "Baa" loudly. The second shepherd responds politely in the same way.

The leader of this song explains the kippers, teaches the verse and demonstrates the greeting. The leader then dances in a swaying style while everyone sings:

Tomorrow we'll have kippers for tea,
Kippers for tea, kippers for tea.
Tomorrow we'll have kippers for tea,
Kippers for tea tomorrow.

The leader then selects another 'shepherd', and greets him or her in Patagonian fashion, and receives a reply. They both dance, one behind the other, while everyone sings again. The second shepherd then chooses a third, and greetings are exchanged.

Complete etiquette then requires that number 2 again greets number 1 before more dancing and singing takes place. By this rule, each time a dancer is added, the greeting is passed all the way down the line. On the other hand, if you are short of time, it is acceptable to omit the multiple greetings!

It's quite daft, but great fun. Try it and see!

THE JOHNSON BOYS

Oh the Johnson boys they built a mill
They built it on the side of a hill.
Oh they worked all night and they worked all day
But they couldn't get the jolly old mill to play.

This verse is sung over again and again, with two variations.
The first note (the word "Oh") is made longer each time, and
the rest is sung faster. Don't forget to start slowly!

ARAM SA SA

This is said to be a traditional song from the Middle East about mounting a camel and galloping away. It is most fun when sung several times, firstly at walking speed, then trotting, then galloping faster and faster.

1. Aram-sa-sa, aram-sa-sa,
    Gali gali gali gali gali ram-sa-sa.
    Aram-sa-sa, aram-sa-sa,
    Gali gali gali gali gali ram-sa-sa.

2. Arami, arami,
    Gali gali gali gali gali ram-sa-sa.
    Arami, arami,
    Gali gali gali gali gali ram-sa-sa.

It is also effective to divide the singers into two groups, so that one sings verse 1 at the same time as the other sings verse 2. If you can manage harmony and speed at the same time you are doing well!

35

NONSENSE AND HUMOUR

THERE WAS A MAN WHO HAD A DOG

There was a man who had a dog
And his name was Bingo.
There was a man who had a dog
And his name was Bingo.
B.I.N.G.O., B.I.N.G.O., B.I.N.G.O. (sing the letter names)
And his name was Bingo.

On the second time through, replace each letter O with a clap.
On the third time, clap instead of G and O.
Continue in the same way until you have a whole line of claps.

MR. PUNCHINELLO

Oh dear mother, I'm to be married to Mr. Punchinello
Oh dear mother, I'm to be married to Mr. Punchinello.
To Mr. Punch, to Mr. Chin, to Mr. Ell, to Mr. O,
Punch-chin-ell-o.

After teaching the song, the leader divides the group into four, calling the parts Mr. Punch, Mr. Chin, Mr. Ell and Mr. O. The song is then sung through slowly. Everyone sings the first two lines, but in lines three and four, each part sings their own bit. The leader helps by pointing. When everyone knows when to come in, start again slowly, and repeat the song continuously, getting faster and faster.

Each verse can begin one note higher than the last.

A GUY HAD A GAME WITH A PING PONG BALL

In this song, a few daft words are sung a great many times to the famous tune from the William Tell Overture by Rossini.

A guy had a game with a ping pong ball
A guy had a game with a ping pong ball
A guy had a game with a ping pong ball
With a ping, with a ping pong ball.

Oh a guy had a game with a ping pong, ping pong, ping pong, ping pong, ping pong ball
With a ping, with a ping, with a ping pong, ping pong, ping pong, ping pong ball.

Ping, ping ping pong, ping ping pong, ping ping ping pong.
Ping, ping ping pong, pine ping pong, ping ping ping pong.

Oh a guy had a game with a ping pong ball
A guy had a game with a ping pong ball
A guy had a game with a ping pong ball
With a ping, with a ping pong ball.

If you get really good at it, try swapping the words ping and pong throughout!

FARMYARD CAROL

This nonsense song involves singing the tune to Good King Wenceslas using the sounds of farm animals. It may sound odd, but it's fun!

First the leader divides the singers into four groups, representing four farmyard animals, e.g. cow (moo), pig (oink), horse (neigh), sheep (baa), duck (quack), dog (woof), etc. Each group only sings when the leader is pointing to them. To begin with, the leader gives each group a long phrase. As they geet the idea, however, the leader jumps unpredictably from group to group, to keep everyone alert!

OH BE KIND TO YOUR WEB-FOOTED FRIENDS

The tune is 'Stars and Stripes', and it needs to be pitched quite low to start with, so it can change into a higher key (as the last line demands).

Oh be kind to your web-footed friends
For that duck may be somebody's mother.
She lives on the edge of a swamp
Where the weather's always damp.
You may think that this is the end.
Well it is, but to prove that I'm a liar,
We're going to sing it again,
Only this time we will sing a little higher.

NURSERY RHYMES THROUGH THE WINDOW

The basic tune to this nonsense song is 'One man went to mow', and the words are nursery rhymes. The words of the chorus are more or less the same each time, with variations to suit the particular rhyme. Here are two examples:

Jack and Jill went up the hill
To fetch a pail of water.
Jack fell down and broke his crown
So she bunged him through the window.

Chorus   The window, the window
She bunged him through the window
Jack fell down and broke his crown
So she bunged him through the window.

Mary had a little lamb
Its fleece was white as snow,
And everywhere that Mary went
She bunged it through the window.

Most nursery rhymes work - ask the singers for suggestions. These are favourites:

Little Jack Horner
Little Miss Muffet
Old Mother Hubbard
Old King Cole
Baa Baa Black Sheep
Simple Simon
Humpty Dumpty
Mary, Mary quite contrary

Save the best one till last, and sing it with due pomp and ceremony:

Pussy cat, pussy cat, where have you been?
I've been up to London to look at the Queen.
Pussy cat, pussy cat, what did you there? (pause for effect)
I bunged her through the window!

FATHER'S PICTURE

These humorous words fit the tune of John Brown's Body.

G
Father's picture hangs on the wall
C   **G**
Next to the picture of the monkey in the hall
           (B7)   **(Em)**
But the greatest puzzle of them all
  A7   **D7**   **G**
Is to find out which is Father!

G
Oh what a compliment to Father
C   **G**
Oh what a compliment to Father
              (B7 Em)
Oh what a compliment to Father
  A7   **D7**   **G**
And one to the monkey too!

THE BOY STOOD ON THE BURNING DECK

These two verses fit the tune of The Happy Wanderer. If you
feel inspired, you could write some more, equally silly of
course!

The boy stood on the burning deck.
Smoke billowed through the air.
"I can't stand any more!" he cried,
And sat down on a chair.

The girl stood on the bridge at night.
Her legs were all a-quiver.
She gave a cough. Her legs fell off
And floated down the river.

THERE WAS AN OLD MAN CALLED MICHAEL FINI-GIN

1. There was an old man called Michael Finigin
   He grew whiskers on his chinigin
   The wind came up and blew them inigin
   Poor old Michael Finigin. Beginigin!

2. There was an old man called Michael Finigin
   He kicked up an awful dinigin
   Because they said he must not singigin
   Poor old Michael Finigin. Beginigin!

3. There was an old man called Michael Finigin
   He went fishing with a pinigin
   Caught a fish but dropped it inigin
   Poor old Michael Finigin. Beginigin!

4. There was an old man called Michael Finigin
   Climbed a tree and barked his shinigin
   Took off several yards of skinigin
   Poor old Michael Finigin. Beginigin!

5. There was an old man called Michael Finigin
   He grew fat and then grew thinigin
   Then he died and had to beginigin
   Poor old Michael Finigin. STOP!

SOAP, SOAP, SOAP AND TOWEL

This is a daft version of the round Row, row, row your boat.

Soap, soap, soap and towel
Flannel and water please.
Merrily, merrily, merrily, merrily
Wash your dirty knees!

ROUNDS

The words and tune to a round are usually short and fairly simple, but it is important that they are thoroughly known and well practised in unison before attempting the harmony version. Here is a suggested routine for successful and enjoyable learning.

First practise all together. Then split into two parts, and let each half sing on their own (a competition, if you like - though for the quality of singing, not the quantity of shouting!). Then sing the round in two parts, indicating clearly when the second part begins. Then swap with the second part going first this time. Then try it twice through. This may be a good time to stop, and come back to it another time. If things are still going well, however, split each half into two and try in four parts.

In this section, the numbers beside the lines of the rounds indicate where second, third or fourth parts can begin.

WHY SHOULDN'T MY GOOSE

1   Why shouldn't my goose
2   Lay as well as thy goose
3   When I paid for my goose
4   Twice as much as thou?

To add a bit of action when the round is well known, ask the singers to put their hands in the air (or stand up, or both) on the highest note - the word goose at the end of the third line. If you are singing in parts, each part will move at a different time, of course.

DONKEYS ARE IN LOVE WITH CARROTS

This round can be sung as a partner song with the last one. In other words, half the singers can sing one song (plus actions), while the other half sing the other song (and do the actions). It can be great fun, but take it in easy steps!

1   Donkeys are in love with carrots
2   Carrots aren't in love at all!
3   Hee-haw, Hee-haw
4   Listen to that loving call!

When the round is well known, add actions in the third line. Raise hands in the air on 'Hee' and back down on 'Haw' each time.

WHOSE PIGS ARE THESE?

1   Whose pigs are these?
2   Whose pigs are these?
3   They are John Pott's, I can tell 'em by the spots, And I
4   found them in the vicarage garden.

THREE BLIND MICE

1   Three blind mice, three blind mice
2   See how they run, see how they run
3   They all ran after the farmer's wife, who cut off their
     tails with a carving knife
4   Did ever you see such a thing in your life as three blind
     mice?

This is fun to sing as a round because the tune and words are
already well-known, but fitting them in is a tongue-twisting
challenge. The faster you sing it, the more challenging it
becomes!

To add to the fun, it can be sung as a partner song with Frere
Jacques. One half of the group sings one song at the same
time as the other half is singing the other!

LIFE IS BUTTER

This play on words is sung to the tune of Frere Jacques.

1   Life is butter, life is butter
2   Melon cauliflower, melon cauliflower
3   Life is butter melon, life is butter melon
4   Cauliflower, cauliflower

Or, more sensibly (and more sadly):

Life is but a melancholy flower (twice)

HEY HO, ANYBODY HOME?

This is supposedly the song of a wandering Canadian lumber-jack:

1   Hey ho! Anybody home?
2   Meat and drink and money have I none
3   But I will be happy!

The word 'happy' at the end is extended over several notes.

FOLK SONGS

IN DUBLIN'S FAIR CITY

To be sung with feeling!

1.
       G   Em
In Dublin's fair city
          Am   D7
Where the girls are so pretty
    G   Em   Am   D7
I first set my eyes on sweet Molly Malone.
     G   Em
She wheeled her wheelbarrow
            Am   D7
Through streets broad and narrow,
            G   Em
Crying, "Cockles and mussels,
  Am   D7 G
Alive alive-o!"

Chorus
                G   Em
"Alive alive-o
           Am   D7
Alive alive-ho!"
                G   Em
Crying, "Cockles and mussels,
      Am   D7 G
Alive alive-o!"

2.   She was a fishmonger
     And sure 'twas no wonder
     For so were her father and mother before.
     They each wheeled their barrow
     Through streets broad and narrow
     Crying, "Cockles and mussels,
     Alive alive-o!"

Chorus

3.   She died of a fever
     And no-one could save her
     And that was the end of sweet Molly Malone.
     But her ghost wheels her barrow
     Through streets broad and narrow
     Crying "Cockles and mussels
     Alive alive-o!"

Chorus

WHAT SHALL WE DO WITH THE DRUNKEN SAILOR?

1.   **Dm**
What shall we do with the drunken sailor

    C
What shall we do with the drunken sailor

    Dm
What shall we do with the drunken sailor

    Am C   Dm
Early in the morning?

Chorus   **Dm**
             Hooray and up she rises

             C
             Hooray and up she rises

             Dm
             Hooray and up she rises

             Am C   Dm
             Early in the morning!

If you want some action, the singers can stand up every time the ship rises up in the chorus. There is a variety of possible punishments for the drunken sailor, of which these are some:

2.   Put him in the scuppers with a hose pipe on him (scuppers = gutters on a ship)

3.   Put him in the long-boat till he's sober

4.   Pull out the plug and wet him all over

5.   Shave him on the belly with a rusty razor

The rusty razor option sounds especially unpleasant! Finish off with:

6.   That's what we'll do with the drunken sailor.

MICHAEL, ROW THE BOAT ASHORE

In the words of this song, St. Michael is rowing the souls of the dead to the heavenly city.

1.   Michael, r**D**ow the boat ashore

G D
Hallelujah.

F#m(D)   **Em**
Michael, row the boat ashore

A7 D
Hallelujah.

2.   Sister, help to trim the sails
Hallelujah.
Sister, help to trim the sails
Hallelujah.

3.   River Jordan is deep and wide
Hallelujah.
Milk and honey on the other side
Hallelujah.

4.   River Jordan is chilly and cold
Hallelujah.
Chills the body but not the soul
Hallelujah.

5.   Repeat verse 1.

THE GIPSY ROVER

1.   The gipsy rover came over the hill
Down to the valley so shady
He whistled and he sang till the green woods rang
And he won the heart of a lady

Chorus   Ah dee doo, ah dee doo dah day
Ah dee doo, ah dee day dee
He whistled and he sang till the green woods rang
And he won the heart of a lady.

2.   She left her father's castle gates
She left her own fond lover
She left her servants and her state
To follow the gipsy rover.

Chorus

3.   Her father saddled his fastest steed
Roamed the valleys all over
Sought his daughter at great speed
And the whistling gipsy rover.

Chorus

4.   He came at last to a mansion fine
      Down by the River Plady
      And there was music and there was wine
      For the gipsy and his lady.

Chorus

5.   "He is no gipsy, my father," she cried,
      "But lord of these lands all over,
      And I will stay till my dying day
      With my whistling gipsy rover."

Chorus

WHEN THE SAINTS GO MARCHING IN

This is another well-known traditional American song about the glories of heaven, but this time in much quicker tempo.

1.   Oh when the **D** saints go marching in

    Oh when the saints go marching **A7** in

    I want to **D** be in that **G** number

    When the **D** saints go **A7** marching **D** in.

2.   Oh when the band begins to play...

3.   Oh when the stars begin to fall....

REFLECTIVE SONGS

HE'S GOT THE WHOLE WORLD IN HIS HANDS

The verses are suggestions only, as this song offers a good opportunity to create verses for a particular group or occasion. The first verse can be sung as a chorus in between verses, or just repeated at the end as a final verse.

1. He's got the whole world in His hands
    He's got the whole world in His hands
    He's got the whole world in His hands
    He's got the whole world in His hands

2. He's got the sun and the moon in His hands....

3. He's got the hills and the rivers in His hands....

4. He's got the rain and sunshine in His hands....

5. He's got every living creature in His hands....

6. He's got the people of all nations in His hands....

GONNA LAY DOWN MY SWORD AND SHIELD

This negro spiritual says that the struggle against evil in this life is a battle worth fighting.

1.   Gonna lay down my sword and shield
Down by the river-side
Down by the river-side
Down by the river-side
Gonna lay down my sword and shield
Down by the river-side
And study war no more.

Chorus   Ain't gonna study war no more (6 times)

2.   Gonna climb the road to Heaven....

3.   Gonna read the Holy Bible....

4.   Gonna fight the wicked devil....

5.   Gonna cross the river of Jordan....

6.   Gonna meet my Lord in Heaven....

ALLELU

This can be sung as a round in two parts, or four:

1. Allelu, allelu, allelu, alleluya
    Praise ye the Lord

2. Allelu, allelu, allelu, alleluya
    Praise ye the Lord

3. Praise ye the Lord, alleluya
    Priase ye the Lord, alleluya

4. Praise ye the Lord, alleluya
    Praise ye the Lord.

FOR HEALTH AND STRENGTH

This short song could be used as a grace before a meal, and can be sung as a round in two or four parts:

1. For health and strength
2. and daily food
3. we praise Thy name
4. O Lord

WE ARE CLIMBING

1.   We are climbing Jesus' ladder
      We are climbing Jesus' ladder
      We are climbing Jesus' ladder
      Children of the Lord

Chorus   Rise and shine and give God the glory, glory
              Rise and shine and give God the glory, glory
              Rise and shine and give God the glory, glory
              Children of the Lord.

2.   Every rung goes higher and higher....

3.   At the top we'll all see Jesus....

In an alternative version, specific youth organisations can refer to their own fellowship and their own aims, for example:

We are climbing Guiding's ladder...
Won't you climb with me?

It is not difficult to compose extra verses to suit the organisation.

A similar song which is adaptable to various organisations is:

We're on the Scouting trail
We're on the Scouting trail
Singing, singing, everybody singing
Scouting bound!

The singers can be divided into two parts, the second part starting one line later, and echoing the first.

GLORIA

This short hymn has a melody and two simple harmony parts, which are not difficult to learn, and sound effective together. The words are in Latin, and mean, "Glory to God in highest Heaven":

Gloria, Gloria, Gloria
In excelsis Deo

YELLS

Yells are an organised form of shouting, and are useful for letting off steam in a controlled and enjoyable way. The other Printforce Campfire books contain plenty of suggestions. Here are a few more.

FIREWORK YELL

Divide the group into four parts, each with a particular sound to make:

1. Sssss, Sssss, Sssss, Sssss (to represent the blue touch paper sizzling)

2. Whoooooooooshhhhhhh (the rocket taking off)

3. Wheeeeeeeeeee (a long whistle)

4. One single loud clap (the aerial explosion)

The leader brings one part in after the other, being particularly careful to co-ordinate the clap. Then everyone says "Aaaaaah" and claps appreciatively.

THERE AIN'T NO FLIES ON US

A simple two-part shout:

1. There ain't no flies on us!

2. There ain't no flies on us!

3. There may be flies on some of you guys

4. But there ain't no flies on us!

OUR BOOTS ARE BIG

Our boots are big
So when we jump
Our big boots go
Thump, thump, thump

Shout the words and stamp loudly on 'jump' and all three 'thumps'.

INDEX